P9-CND-632

Usborne

# 100 Paper Spaceships

## to fold & fly

Illustrated by Andy Tudor

Designed by Hannah Ahmed
and Brian Voakes

Turn over for tips on folding,
flying and storing
your paper spaceships.

# Useful tips

Here are some helpful tips that will make your spaceships fly more effectively and keep them in good shape.

## How to launch your paper spaceship

Here are the best steps to a perfect take-off and landing:

- Stand facing forward.

- Hold each spaceship just in front of its midpoint.

- Pull back and then throw forward in a long, smooth movement to release your spaceship.

## Folding

- Use a ruler to line up the folds and keep them sharp.

- If you want to keep your spaceship for another day, store it flat inside a book.

- If your spaceship gets wet, or won't fly... fold a new one!

## Flying

- Try changing the angle of your spaceship's wings to alter its flight.

Wings up

Wings down

Add a wing tip fold.